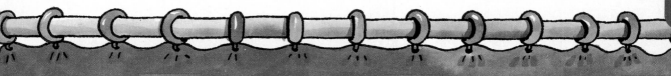

7 + 2 = ☐   5 add 1 = ☐   3 and 7 = ☐

6 and 3 = ☐   0 + 7 = ☐   2 add 6 = ☐

5 add 3 = ☐   4 and 6 = ☐    = ☐

Colour 3 🏺 to make 10.

2   5   4   3

Colour 3 🕰 to make 9.

 1    6    2    3

3 + ☐ = 5   ☐ + 1 = 10

8 + ☐ = 9   ☐ + 5 = 7

6 + ☐ = 6   ☐ + 4 = 6

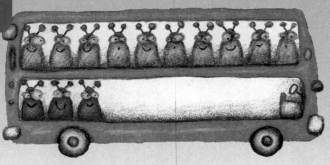 

10 + 3 = _____   _____ + _____ = _____

3 + 10 = _____   _____ + _____ = _____

10 + 6 = ☐   10 + 4 = ☐   5 + 10 = ☐

10 + 9 = ☐   6 + 10 = ☐   10 + 5 = ☐

1 + 10 = ☐   9 + 10 = ☐

10 + ☐ = 12   10 + ☐ = 17

☐ + 10 = 14   ☐ + 10 = 20

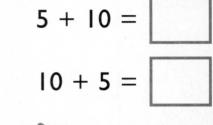

add 1

16 ⟶ ☐

13 ⟶ ☐

19 ⟶ ☐

add 2

14 ⟶ ☐

11 ⟶ ☐

18 ⟶ ☐

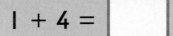
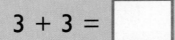

1 + 4 =	3 + 3 =	2 + 2 =
3 + 4 =	6 + 1 =	1 + 8 =
4 + 5 =	10 + 0 =	4 + 2 =
0 + 8 =	4 + 4 =	2 + 3 =

Match.

7 + 1	5 + 2	3 + 5	5 + 5

3 + 6	7 + 0	1 + 9	2 + 7

How many altogether?

4 + 3 =

Use cubes.

 + 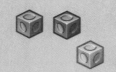 $14 + 3 =$

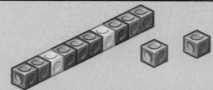 +  $12 + 4 =$

$14 + 4 =$ ☐ $16 + 3 =$ ☐ $11 + 4 =$ ☐

$15 + 5 =$ ☐ $2 + 17 =$ ☐ $12 + 6 =$ ☐

$4 + 5 =$

$14 + 5 =$

$2 + 7 =$

$12 + 7 =$

$13 + 2 =$ ☐ $17 + 1 =$ ☐ $13 + 6 =$ ☐

$8 + 11 =$ ☐ $18 + 0 =$ ☐ $12 + 8 =$ ☐

$11 + 3 =$ ☐ $4 + 15 =$ ☐ $12 + 5 =$ ☐

$0 + 16 =$ ☐ $11 + 9 =$ ☐ $5 + 13 =$ ☐

Match to make 17.

 6

 11

 15

 4

 2

13

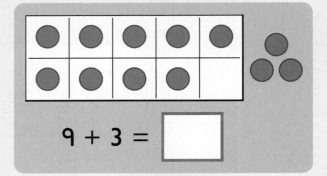

9 + 3 = ☐

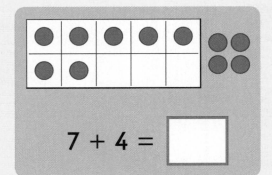

7 + 4 = ☐

9 + 5 = ☐   8 + 6 = ☐   9 + 4 = ☐

8 + 4 = ☐   7 + 5 = ☐   8 + 3 = ☐

5 + 7 = ____   5 + 8 = ____   4 + 7 = ____

4 + 8 = ____   9 + 2 = ____   6 + 8 = ____

9 + 6 = ____   3 + 8 = ____   8 + 5 = ____

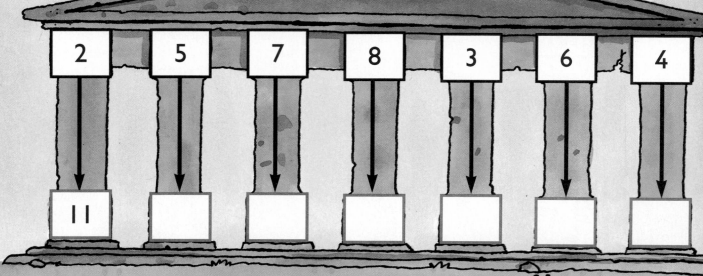

Add 9.

2	5	7	8	3	6	4
11						

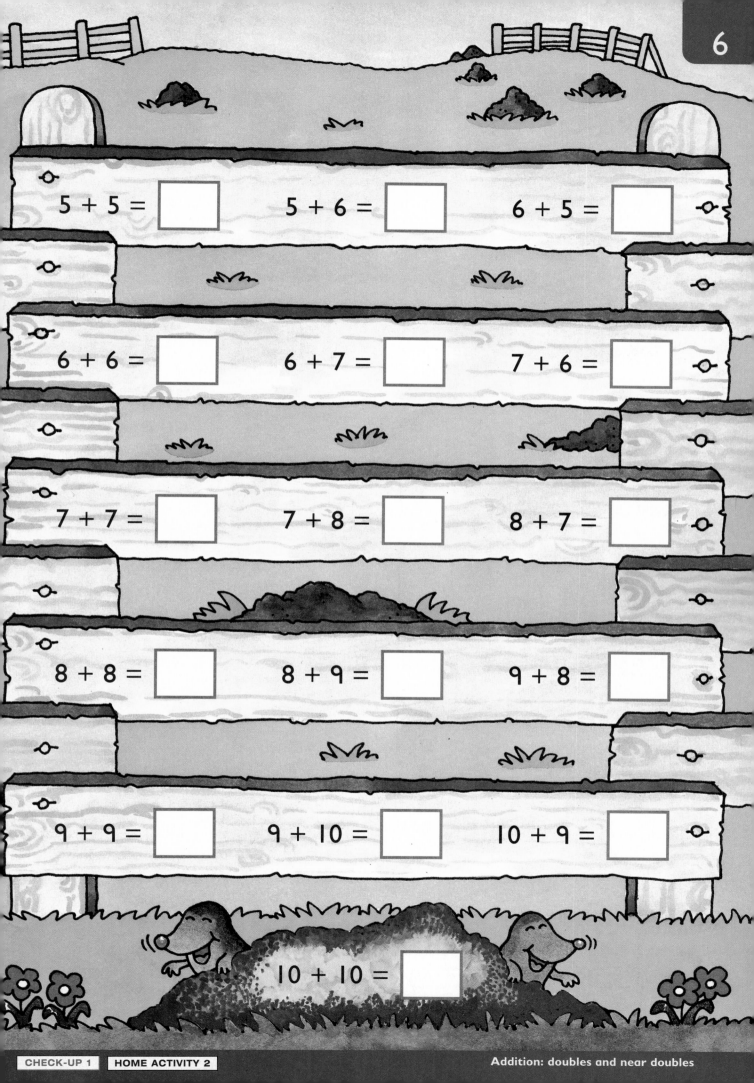

5 + 5 = ☐   5 + 6 = ☐   6 + 5 = ☐

6 + 6 = ☐   6 + 7 = ☐   7 + 6 = ☐

7 + 7 = ☐   7 + 8 = ☐   8 + 7 = ☐

8 + 8 = ☐   8 + 9 = ☐   9 + 8 = ☐

9 + 9 = ☐   9 + 10 = ☐   10 + 9 = ☐

10 + 10 = ☐

$9 + 2 =$

$2 + 9 =$

$ + =$

$ + =$

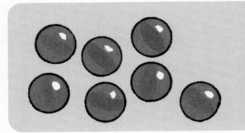 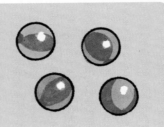

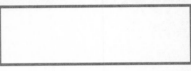

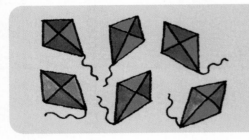 

$\boxed{} + 3 = 11$ $\qquad$ $\boxed{} + 6 = 11$ $\qquad$ $\boxed{} + 4 = 11$

$9 + \boxed{} = 11$ $\qquad$ $2 + \boxed{} = 11$ $\qquad$ $3 + \boxed{} = 11$

Colour two to make 11.

Use cubes. Make 12.

8 + ☐

5 + ☐

7 + ☐

4 + ☐

9 + ☐

6 + ☐

3 + ☐

7 + 5 = ☐

9 + 3 = ☐

5 + 6 = ☐

5 + 7 = ☐

4 + 8 = ☐

3 + 9 = ☐

Match.

6 + 6

8 add 3

9 and 3

8 + 4

3 + 9

4 add 8

4 + 7

5 and 7

9 + ☐ = 12   7 + ☐ = 12   ☐ + 6 = 12

How many?

Add.

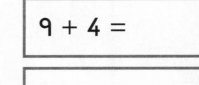

$9 + 4 =$

$4 + 9 =$

$+ \quad =$

$+ \quad =$

$+ \quad =$

$+ \quad =$

$5 + 8 =$ ☐ $7 + 6 =$ ☐ $4 + 9 =$ ☐

$7 + 5 =$ ☐ $9 + 4 =$ ☐ $8 + 5 =$ ☐

$6 +$ ☐ $= 13$ $9 +$ ☐ $= 13$

☐ $+ 5 = 13$ ☐ $+ 7 = 13$

$$7 + 7 =$$

$$9 + 5 =$$ $$\quad + \quad =$$

Draw 1 more .

$$\quad + \quad =$$ $$\quad + \quad =$$

$$\quad + \quad =$$ $$\quad + \quad =$$

Draw 1 more .

$$\quad + \quad =$$ $$\quad + \quad =$$

$$5 + 9 = \boxed{}$$ $$7 + 7 = \boxed{}$$ $$9 + 6 = \boxed{}$$

$$8 + 6 = \boxed{}$$ $$9 + 4 = \boxed{}$$ $$7 + 8 = \boxed{}$$

$$9 + \boxed{} = 14$$ $$8 + \boxed{} = 15$$

$$\boxed{} + 9 = 15$$ $$\boxed{} + 7 = 14$$

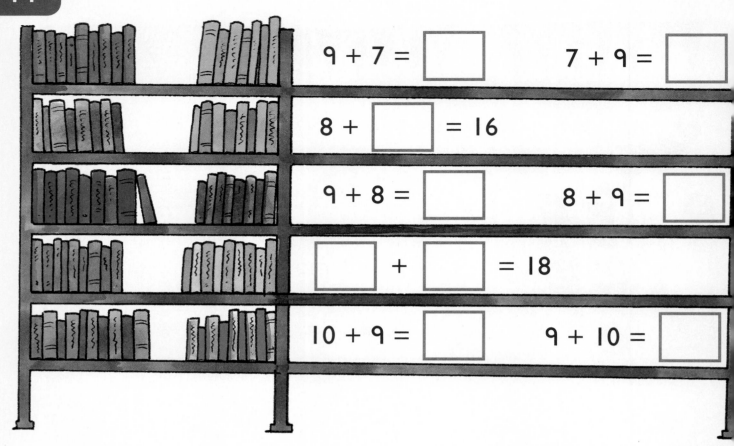

9 + 7 = ☐   7 + 9 = ☐

8 + ☐ = 16

9 + 8 = ☐   8 + 9 = ☐

☐ + ☐ = 18

10 + 9 = ☐   9 + 10 = ☐

9 + ☐ = 16   9 + ☐ = 17

8 + ☐ = 16   8 + ☐ = 17

☐ + 7 = 16

10 + ☐ = 19

9 + ☐ = 18   9 + ☐ = 19

9   7

_____ books altogether.

8   8

_____ books altogether.

 + = 20

□ + □ = 20

□ + □ = 20

Make 20.

□ + 10

19 + □

□ + 5

4 + □

□ + 9

20

8 + □

□ + 13

2 + □

□ + 3

6 + □

Addition: facts for 20

6 + 8 = _____   9 + 2 = _____   8 + 8 = _____

9 + 6 = _____   5 + 7 = _____   3 + 8 = _____

4 + 7 = _____   3 + 9 = _____   9 + 4 = _____

6 + 7 = _____   7 + 9 = _____   8 + 6 = _____

8 + ☐ = 11   16 + ☐ = 20   4 + ☐ = 13

Colour two .

Make 12.   Make 18.

Make 20.   Make 15.

$3 + 7 + 5 =$ ___ $8 + 2 + 7 =$ ___

$6 + 7 + 4 =$ ___ $5 + 8 + 3 =$ ___

$4 + 9 + 3 =$ ___ $7 + 5 + 7 =$ ___

$8 + 1 + 9 =$ ___ $3 + 5 + 6 =$ ___

$9 + 5 + \boxed{} = 16$ $4 + \boxed{} + 6 = 13$

Find the totals.

Make 20.

Make 20.

Choose three numbers each time ⟶
Make different totals.

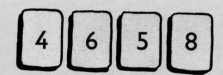

+	+	=

+	+	=

+	+	=

+	+	=

Use ☐9☐ ☐3☐ ☐6☐ ☐8☐ .

Make one wheel number and colour it.

14   ☐ + ☐   20

16   ☐ + ☐   12

15   ☐ + ☐   13

17   ☐ + ☐   11

Colour even numbers  🚗 and odd numbers 🚗 .

5   10   8   7

9   4   3   2

Make 12. Use two 🚗 . _____

Make 12. Use two 🚗 . _____

Make 14. Use two 🚗 and one 🚗 .

_____

10p 7p 5p 8p 12p 4p

How much?

 ☐ p

 ☐ p

 ☐ p

Spend 19p. Draw what you can buy.

Find three different ways to spend 15p.

Write the missing numbers.

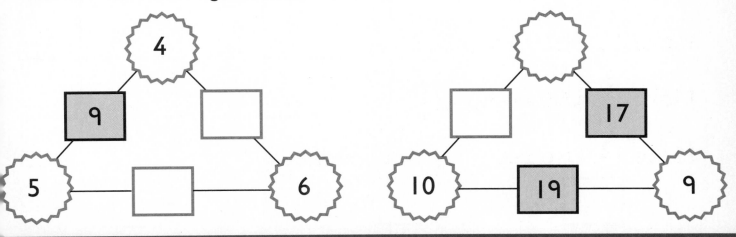

1

$5 + 5 =$ ☐ $4 + 5 =$ ☐ $6 + 3 =$ ☐

$8 + 2 =$ ☐ $6 + 4 =$ ☐ $2 + 6 =$ ☐

$3 + 5 =$ ☐ $1 + 6 =$ ☐ $3 + 4 =$ ☐

2

$10 + 6 =$ ☐ $10 + 4 =$ ☐ $7 + 10 =$ ☐

$10 +$ ☐ $= 15$ ☐ $+ 10 = 13$

$10 +$ ☐ $= 18$ ☐ $+ 10 = 20$

3 Find each total.

$14 + 1 =$ ☐ $4 + 16 =$ ☐ $15 + 3 =$ ☐

$2 + 17 =$ ☐ $13 + 3 =$ ☐ $8 + 11 =$ ☐

$12 + 2 =$ ☐ $6 + 11 =$ ☐ $14 + 6 =$ ☐

4 How many altogether?

$5 + 8 =$ ☐ $9 + 4 =$ ☐ $7 + 5 =$ ☐

$8 + 3 =$ ☐ $6 + 7 =$ ☐ $3 + 9 =$ ☐

$6 + 5 =$ ☐ $4 + 8 =$ ☐ $6 + 6 =$ ☐

$4 +$ ☐ $= 13$ ☐ $+ 4 = 11$ $5 +$ ☐ $= 12$

1 How many altogether?

9 add 9 = ☐   7 add 8 = ☐   5 add 9 = ☐

8 add 6 = ☐   10 add 9 = ☐   8 add 9 = ☐

7 add 9 = ☐   8 add 7 = ☐   9 add 6 = ☐

☐ + 7 = 14   8 + ☐ = 16   9 + ☐ = 17

2 Make 20.

10 +		+ 8		17 +

| + | | + | | + |

3 Find each total.

3 + 7 + 5 = ☐   6 + 7 + 4 = ☐

Colour three numbers each time.

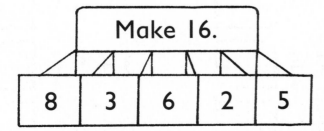

Make 16.

8   3   6   2   5

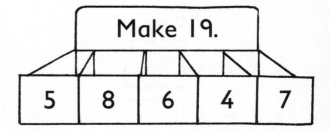

Make 19.

5   8   6   4   7

Colour to match.

5 – 2	4 – 2
7 – 0	6 – 1
2 – 1	4 – 0
7 – 1	6 – 6

0	1	2
3		4
5	6	7

Match.

6 take away 3   5 subtract 4   6 less than 7

 2   **3**   **1**   **4**

6 subtract 4   5 less than 7   7 take away 3

$3 - 1 = \boxed{}$ $4 - 3 = \boxed{}$ $5 - 5 = \boxed{}$

$6 - 0 = \boxed{}$ $6 - 5 = \boxed{}$ $5 - 3 = \boxed{}$

$7 - 7 = \boxed{}$ $3 - 0 = \boxed{}$ $7 - 4 = \boxed{}$

$\boxed{} - 1 = 4$ $\boxed{} - 2 = 5$ $\boxed{} - 4 = 0$

6 fall off. | – 6 =
3 fall off. | – =

Colour to match.

9 take away 2

8 take away 4

Subtract 10 from 10.

The difference
between
10 and 5.

10 subtract 8

Take 8 from 9.

3 less than 9

The difference
between
5 and 8.

0	7
1	6
2	5
3	4

 9
 7
 4

How many more than | – =

than ? | – =

10 – 2 = ☐   8 – 1 = ☐   10 – 0 = ☐

8 – 7 = ☐   9 – 0 = ☐   8 – 8 = ☐

9 – ☐ = 4   10 – ☐ = 6   ☐ – ☐ = 3

Use cubes.

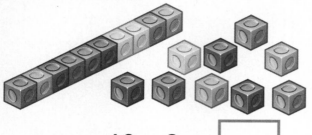

$19 - 3 = \boxed{}$

$16 - 4 = \boxed{}$

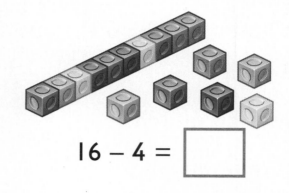

$18 - 7 = \underline{}$

$17 - 4 = \underline{}$

$17 - 6 = \boxed{}$

$19 - 8 = \underline{}$

$4 - 3 =$	$9 - 2 =$	$7 - 5 =$
$14 - 3 =$	$19 - 2 =$	$17 - 5 =$

$19 - 4 = \underline{}$	$17 - 3 = \underline{}$	$18 - 6 = \underline{}$
$14 - 2 = \underline{}$	$19 - 7 = \underline{}$	$15 - 0 = \underline{}$
$18 - 3 = \underline{}$	$12 - 2 = \underline{}$	$15 - 4 = \underline{}$

Make 14.

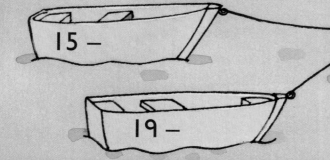

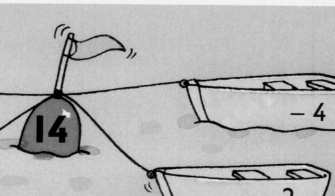

15 –

19 –

– 4

– 2

14

10 − 7 =

20 − 7 =

10 − 9 =

20 − 9 =

10 − 4 =

20 − 4 =

20 − 2 = _____

20 − 10 = _____

20 − 8 = _____

20 − 3 = _____

20 − 1 = _____

20 − 6 = _____

subtract 3

subtract 5

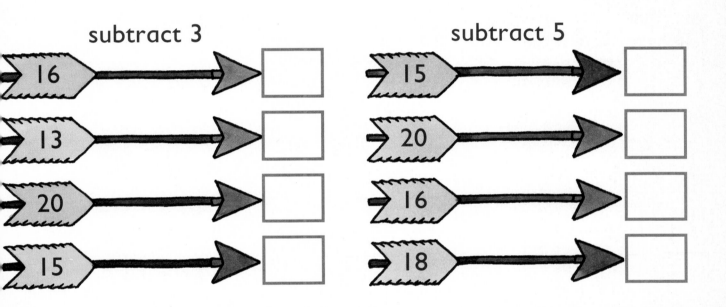

14 − 1 = ☐

15 − ☐ = 13

☐ − 1 = 16

17 − 2 = ☐

20 − ☐ = 20

☐ − 4 = 10

19 − 6 = ☐

18 − ☐ = 16

☐ − 2 = 11

Use cubes.

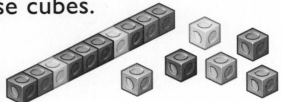 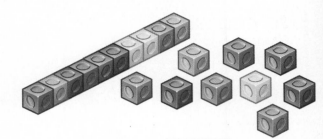

16 − 11 = ☐   19 − 13 = ☐

18 − 15 = ☐   15 − 13 = ☐   17 − 12 = ☐

16 − ☐ = 3   15 − ☐ = 0   12 − ☐ = 1

| 4 − 1 = | 9 − 7 = | 8 − 3 = |
| 14 − 11 = | 19 − 17 = | 18 − 13 = |

15 − 12 = ☐   13 − 11 = ☐   17 − 13 = ☐

19 − 14 = ☐   16 − 16 = ☐   18 − 14 = ☐

16 − 12 = ☐   18 − 12 = ☐   19 − 10 = ☐

Find the difference between

17 and 14 ____   18 and 16 ____

14 and 10 ____   17 and 15 ____

Use cubes.

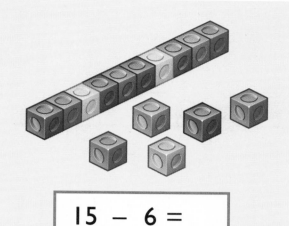

15 − 6 =

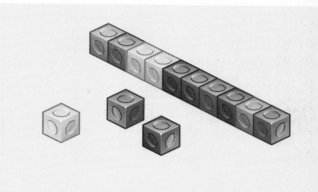

13 − 5 =

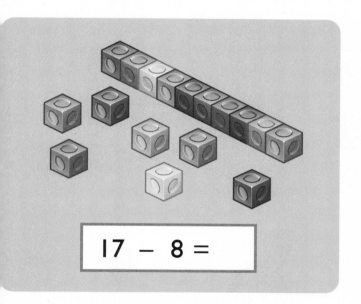

17 − 8 =

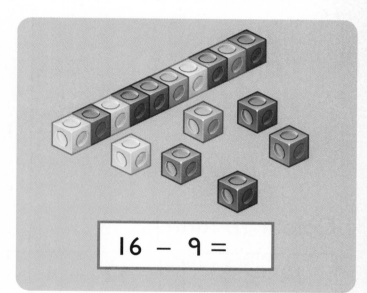

16 − 9 =

14 − 6 = ☐   17 − 9 = ☐   15 − 9 = ☐

11 − 6 = ☐   14 − 7 = ☐   15 − 8 = ☐

12 − 4 = ☐   12 − 7 = ☐   13 − 7 = ☐

11 minus 8 = ☐   12 subtract 5 = ☐

Take 6 from 13. ☐   Subtract 9 from 14. ☐

$15 - 7 = \boxed{}$

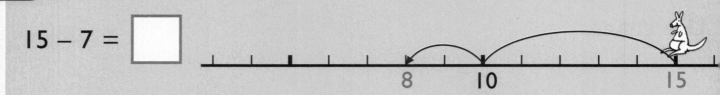

$14 - 8 = \boxed{}$

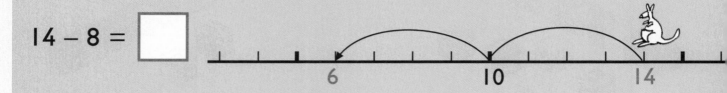

$13 - 5 = \boxed{}$ $16 - 7 = \boxed{}$ $14 - 5 = \boxed{}$

$16 - 9 = \boxed{}$ $15 - 8 = \boxed{}$ $13 - 8 = \boxed{}$

$12 - 6 = \boxed{}$ $14 - 7 = \boxed{}$

$16 - 8 = \boxed{}$ $18 - 9 = \boxed{}$

Colour to match.

12 – 3	12 – 4
11 – 5	11 – 2
11 – 4	12 – 5
13 – 4	11 – 3

$11 - 8 = \boxed{}$ $13 - 9 = \boxed{}$ $11 - 7 = \boxed{}$

$12 - 9 = \boxed{}$ $11 - 9 = \boxed{}$ $12 - 8 = \boxed{}$

How many 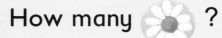 ? ☐

$11 - 2 =$ ☐ $11 - 3 =$ ☐

$11 - 4 =$ ☐
$11 - 5 =$ ☐ $11 - 6 =$ ☐ $11 - 7 =$ ☐

$11 - 8 =$ ☐ $11 - 9 =$ ☐

Colour to match.

$11 - 4$	11 take away 2
$11 - 9$	11 subtract 7
$11 - 6$	Take 3 from 11.

$11 - 8 =$ ☐ $11 - 5 =$ ☐ $11 - 11 =$ ☐

4 less than $11 =$ ☐   Subtract 9 from 11. ☐

11 minus $6 =$ ☐   1 less than $11 =$ ☐

$11 -$ ☐ $= 7$ $11 -$ ☐ $= 9$ $11 -$ ☐ $= 11$

How many hats? ____

12 − 3 = ☐

12 − 4 = ☐   12 − 5 = ☐

12 − 6 = ☐   12 − 7 = ☐

12 − 8 = ☐   12 − 9 = ☐

4 are sold.
How many are left? ☐

7 are sold.
How many are left? ☐

12 − 9 = ☐   12 − 3 = ☐   12 − 0 = ☐

12 take away 8 = ☐   12 subtract 5 = ☐

9 less than 12 = ☐   12 minus 12 = ☐

Take 6 from 12. ☐   Subtract 4 from 12. ☐

12 − ☐ = 5   12 − ☐ = 4   12 − ☐ = 7

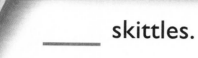

____ skittles.

____ fall down.

How many are left? ____

$13 - 4 = \boxed{}$

$13 - 5 = \boxed{}$　　　$13 - 6 = \boxed{}$　　　$13 - 7 = \boxed{}$

$13 - 8 = \boxed{}$　　　$13 - 9 = \boxed{}$　　　$13 - 10 = \boxed{}$

13 take away 5 = ____　　　　Take 9 from 13. ____

13 subtract 7 = ____　　　　Subtract 6 from 13. ____

13 minus 8 = ____　　　　4 less than 13 ____

$13 - \boxed{} = 4$　　　　　　$13 - \boxed{} = 6$

$13 - \boxed{} = 8$　　　　　　$13 - \boxed{} = 9$

$13 - \boxed{} = 5$　　　　　　$13 - \boxed{} = 7$

$13 - \boxed{} = 10$　　　　　$13 - \boxed{} = 13$

How many ?

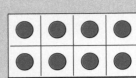   

14 − 4 = ☐   14 − 5 = ☐   14 − 8 = ☐

14 − 7 = ☐   14 − 9 = ☐   14 − 6 = ☐

How many ○ ? ☐

15 − 6 = ☐   15 − 9 = ☐   15 − 7 = ☐

15 − 8 = ☐   15 − 5 = ☐   15 − 10 = ☐

Colour to match.

Subtract 6 from 15

6

7 less than 14

9

7

14 minus 8

14 − ☐ = 9   15 − ☐ = 8   ☐ − 9 = 6

15 − ☐ = 7   14 − ☐ = 5   ☐ − 6 = 8

16

16 − 6 = _____

16 − 7 = _____   16 − 8 = _____   16 − 9 = _____

17

17 − 10 = _____

17 − 7 = _____   17 − 8 = _____   17 − 9 = _____

18

18 − 10 = _____

18 − 9 = _____

18 − 8 = _____

19

19 − 9 = _____

19 − 10 = _____

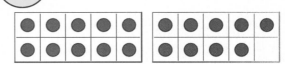

10 less than 16 _____

8 less than 18 _____

9 less than 16 _____

Make 9.

Make 8.

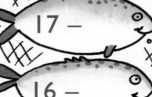

_____ − 9   _____ − 8

17 −   19 −

16 −   18 −

20 − 16 = ___   20 − 12 = ___   20 − 15 = ___

20 − 13 = ___   20 − 18 = ___   20 − 11 = ___

20 − 19 = ___   20 − 17 = ___   20 − 14 = ___

```
|----|----|----|----|----|----|----|----|----|----|
10   11   12   13   14   15   16   17   18   19   20
```

20 − 5 = [   ]   20 − 2 = [   ]   20 − 8 = [   ]

20 − [   ] = 17   20 − [   ] = 14   20 − [   ] = 16

20 − [   ] = 11   20 − [   ] = 19   20 − [   ] = 13

Match.

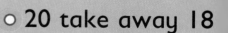

Take 14 from 20 ○   2   ○ 20 take away 18

4 less than 20 ○   12   ○ 8 less than 20

                          6

20 minus 17 ○   3   ○ 20 subtract 0

                          16

                          20

15 − 6 = ☐   13 − 8 = ☐   11 − 5 = ☐

13 − 7 = ☐   18 − 10 = ☐   14 − 9 = ☐

12 − 3 = ☐   16 − 6 = ☐   17 − 17 = ☐

15 take away 8 = ☐   13 minus 4 = ☐

14 subtract 6 = ☐   12 subtract 8 = ☐

6 less than 13 = ☐   9 less than 16 = ☐

Take 10 from 14. ☐   Subtract 7 from 15. ☐

Colour to match.

11 − 3 = ☐   14 − 8 = ☐   13 − 10 = ☐

16 − 8 = ☐   12 − 7 = ☐   17 − 9 = ☐

13 − 13 = ☐   15 − 9 = ☐   18 − 8 = ☐

Find the difference in age.

I am 13.

I am 9.

☐ − ☐ = ☐

I am 7.

I am 14.

☐ − ☐ = ☐

11 take away 2 = ☐   18 minus 9 = ☐

16 subtract 7 = ☐   4 less than 20 = ☐

Take 10 from 16. ☐   Subtract 9 from 11. ☐

13 − ☐ = 8

☐ − 6 = 5

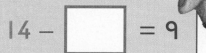

14 − ☐ = 9

☐ − 9 = 3

9 + 2 = ____

2 + 9 = ____

11 − 2 = ____

11 − 9 = ____

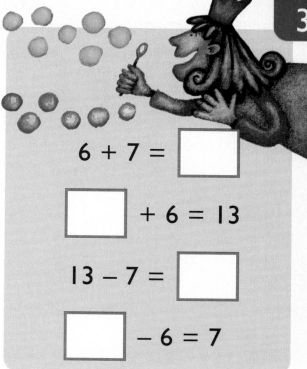

6 + 7 = ☐

☐ + 6 = 13

13 − 7 = ☐

☐ − 6 = 7

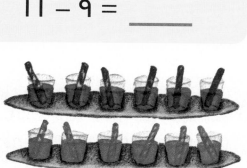

6 + 6 = ☐

12 − 6 = ☐

7 + 7 = ☐

14 − ☐ = 7

4   +   8   =   12

____ + ____ = ____

____ − ____ = ____

____ − ____ = ____

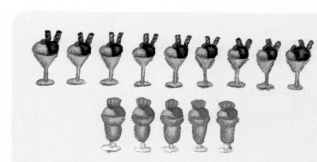

9   +   5   =   14

____ + ____ = ____

____ − ____ = ____

____ − ____ = ____

$$8 + 7 = 15$$

___ + ___ = ___

___ − ___ = ___

___ − ___ = ___

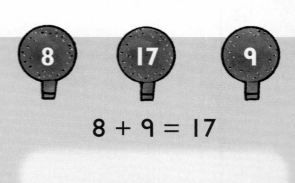

$$8 + 9 = 17$$

___

___

___

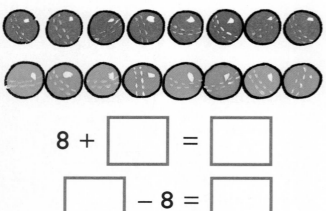

$$8 + \boxed{} = \boxed{}$$

$$\boxed{} - 8 = \boxed{}$$

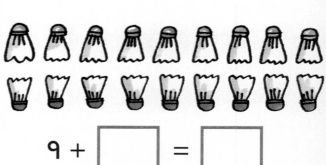

$$9 + \boxed{} = \boxed{}$$

$$\boxed{} - 9 = \boxed{}$$

___

___

___

___

___

___

___

___

Sort.

16	8	✔
11	16
7	15

20	11
18	13
19	11

17	9
20	12
9	16

| difference of 8 | ~~difference of 8~~ |

| 16 | 8 |

Find my number.

 9 more than 6.

The difference between 12 and 20.

Write a clue.

 | 14 |

Use | 17 | 16 | 15 | 7 | 8

Complete.

☐ – ☐ = 7   ☐ – 7 = 8

☐ – ☐ = 9   ☐ – ☐ = 9

| 5 less than 18 | | 4 more than 8 |

☐ minus 6   Take 5 from ☐

5 + 2 + ☐   Subtract ☐ from 20

Sal   Joe

Who has double 6 add 1? _____

1

6 − 3 = ☐   7 − 5 = ☐   5 − 2 = ☐

8 − 4 = ☐   9 − 0 = ☐   10 − 6 = ☐

Subtract 3 from 9. ____   5 less than 10 is ____.

2

19 − 4 = ☐   18 − 6 = ☐   15 − 4 = ☐

17 − 5 = ☐   20 − 8 = ☐   16 − 2 = ☐

20 − ☐ = 13   ☐ − 1 = 18   14 − ☐ = 11

3

19 − 15 = ☐   17 − 12 = ☐   16 − 14 = ☐

18 − 18 = ☐   15 − 11 = ☐   19 − 13 = ☐

Find the difference between

14 and 11 ____   18 and 12 ____   17 and 13 ____

4

11 − 6 = ☐   13 − 7 = ☐   12 − 5 = ☐

13 − 9 = ☐   12 − 4 = ☐   11 − 8 = ☐

12 minus 8. ____   7 less than 11 is ____.

13 − ☐ = 7   11 − ☐ = 8   ☐ − 6 = 6

Subtraction: assessment

1   14 – 6 = ☐   15 – 9 = ☐   14 – 8 = ☐

15 – 7 = ☐   14 – 5 = ☐   15 – 6 = ☐

 14   7   How many more  ? ____

14 – ☐ = 5   15 – ☐ = 7   15 – ☐ = 10

2   17 – 9 = ☐   16 – 7 = ☐   16 – 8 = ☐

18 – 9 = ☐   17 – 8 = ☐   19 – 9 = ☐

Subtract 9 from 16. ____   Take 7 from 17. ____

3   20 – 13 = ☐   20 – 9 = ☐   20 – 16 = ☐

Find the difference between

20 and 17 ____   20 and 8 ____   7 and 20 ____

 Match.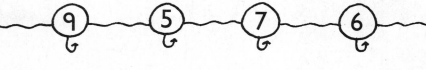

Subtraction: assessment

Published by Heinemann Educational Publishers, Halley Court, Jordan Hill, Oxford OX2 8EJ,
a division of Reed Educational and Professional Publishers Ltd.
ISBN 0 435 16975 0 © Scottish Primary Mathematics Group 1999.
First published 1999.   03 02   10 9 8 7 6 5 4
Designed and illustrated by Gecko Ltd. Printed by Pindar plc, Scarborough.

ISBN 0-435-16975-0

9 780435 169749